INTERMEDIATE

CONTENTS:

ISBN-10: 0-8497-9757-8

ISBN-13: 978-0-8497-9757-6

You Have to Shake It

Ross Petot

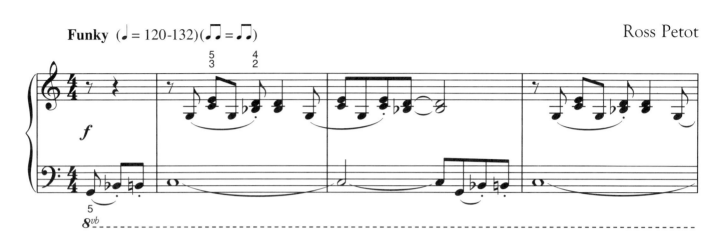

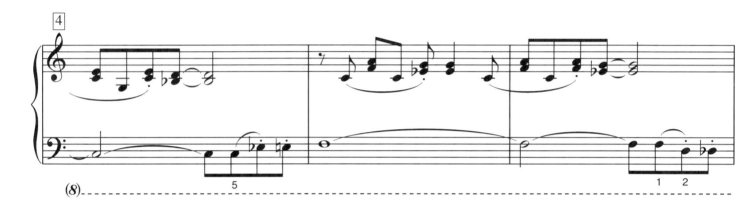

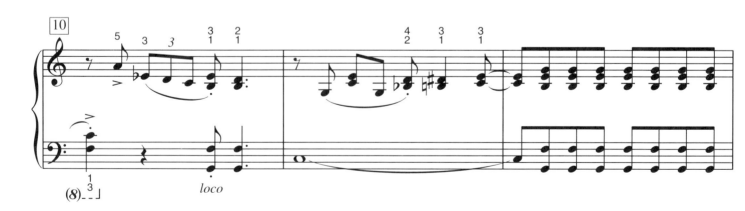

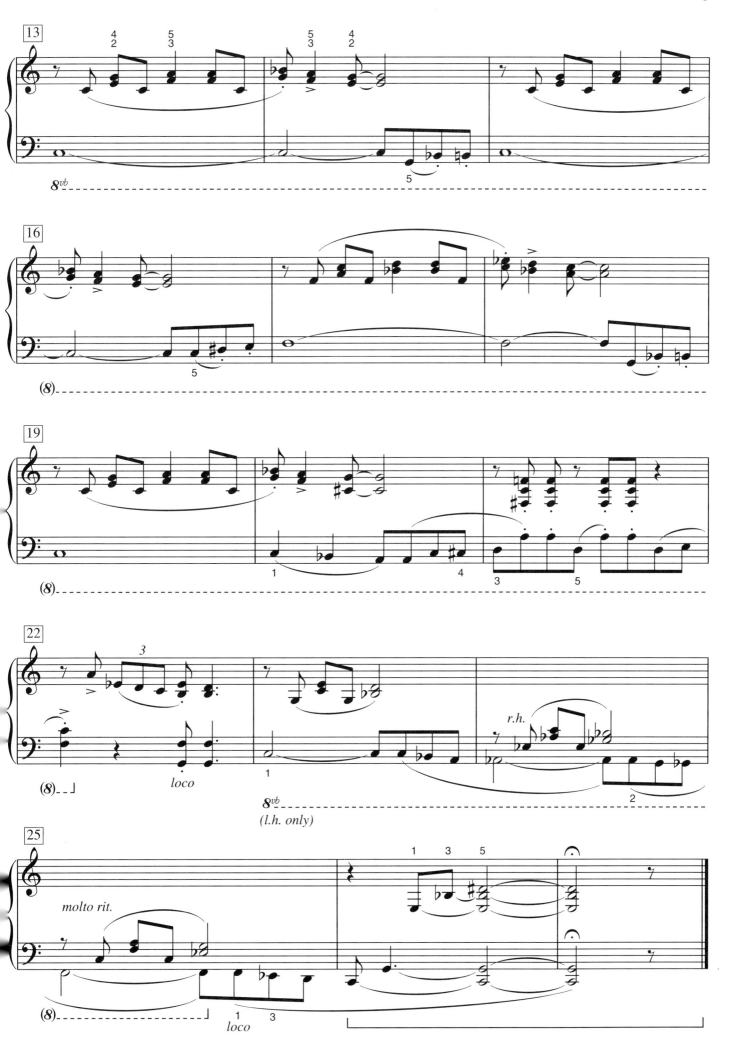

THE NEWTONVILLE BOUNCE

Ross Petot

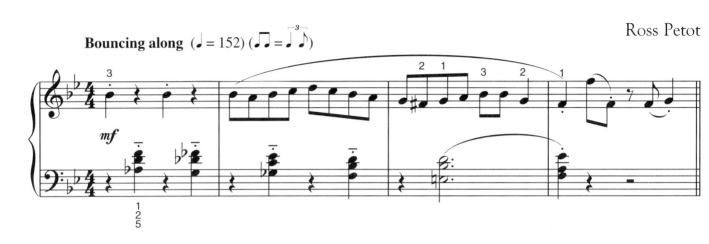

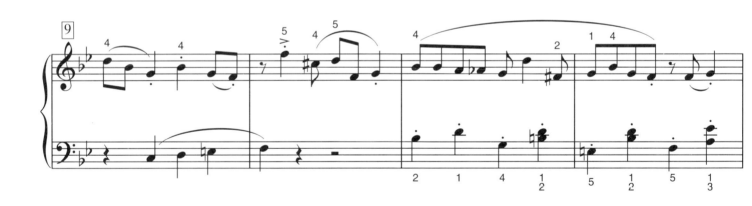

Safe Passage

Moderately ($\quad$ = ca. 112)

Ross Petot

TEN O'CLOCK GROOVE

Ross Petot

Medium Rock (♩ = ca. 120)

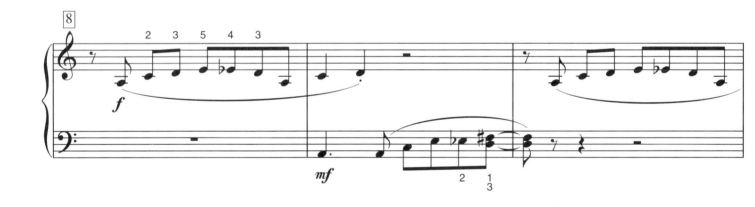

© 2010 Kjos Music Press, 4382 Jutland Drive, San Diego, California 92117.

You've Got to Be Kidding

Ross Petot

WP607

THE HORN BLOWER

Ross Petot

Swamp Rat

Ross Petot

Outta Sight

Medium Rock (♩ = 120) (♪♪ = ♪♪)

Ross Petot

Good Choice

Ross Petot

STAY A WHILE

Ross Petot

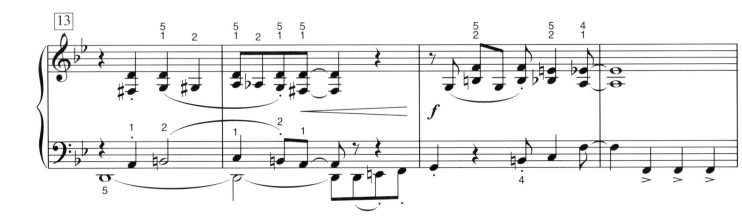